Barker

SCHOOL

Jeanne Willis
Illustrated by Margaret Chamberlain

My dog likes sleeping.
My dog likes eating.
But most of all, he likes to bark.

"Stop barking!" says Mum.

3

He barks at the postman.
He barks at the dustman.
He barks at the snowman.

"Stop barking!" says Dad.

When we go to the park,
my dog likes playing.
But most of all, he likes to bark.

He barks at the bikes.
He barks at the balls.
He barks at the ducks.
"Stop barking!" says the park keeper.

When we go to the farm,
my dog likes running.
But most of all, he likes to bark.

He barks at the hens.
He barks at the cows.
He barks at the sheep.
"Stop barking!" says the farmer.

When we go to the shops,
my dog likes sniffing.
But most of all, he likes to bark.

He barks at the butcher.
He barks at the baker.
He barks at the window cleaner.
"Stop barking!" say the people.

When we go back home,
my dog likes yawning,
my dog likes snoring.

But most of all, he likes to bark.
He barks at the front door.
He barks at the back door.

He barks at the window.

WOOF
WOOF
WOOF

"Good dog!" says Dad.
"Good dog!" says Mum.
"You can bark as much as you like!"